FOLKLORE OF AMERICAN WEATHER

Books by ERIC SLOANE

Clouds, Air and Wind

Camouflage Simplified

Skies and the Artist

Your Body in Flight

Eric Sloane's Weather Book

American Barns and Covered Bridges

Our Vanishing Landscape

Seasons of America Past

American Yesterday

Return to Taos

Eric Sloane's Almanac and Weather Forecaster

The Book of Storms

Look at the Sky!

Diary of an Early American Boy

Folklore of American Weather

Folklore of American Weather

by

ERIC SLOANE

DUELL, SLOAN AND PEARCE

New York

Copyright © 1963 by Eric Sloane

Second Printing, August, 1963

Affiliate of
MEREDITH PRESS
Des Moines & New York

Library of Congress Catalogue Card Number: 63-10342

MANUFACTURED IN THE UNITED STATES OF AMERICA FOR MEREDITH PRESS

VAN REES PRESS • NEW YORK

Contents

To Ruth, the setter of my barograph and chief tester of my weather folklore. Champion of honesty and exactness, she gave this book her stalwart help, without which it would have been finished a darn sight sooner.

FOLKLORE OF AMERICAN WEATHER

Author's note.

Folklore can be a very loose word, used to cover a lack of knowledge of the very thing that folklore means. When there is nothing else to attribute a hearsay belief to, it so often becomes branded as genuine folklore. I recall hearing about an early inn known as The Bag of Nails, which was supposed to have been named Bag-o'-nails Inn many years ago. Folklore had contrived many tales about the early hand-made-nail makers and how they used to "pay off their inn bills by exchanging bags of nails." Yet after research it was found that the inn was first called The Bacchanalian. The farmers had found that name a bit too difficult, and it was probably by purposeful mispronunciation that it became called the Bag-o'-nails. The final inn sign displayed a cloth bag with nails in it!

Another time, when I was writing about early-American weathervanes, I related, tongue-in-cheek, an old Maine story of how down east they used to hang a heavy chain on a tall pole. "When that chain stood straight out," the story goes, "the old-timers knew there was a wind a-blowin'." You can imagine my amazement when later I found an article written on weathervanes that had taken my story seriously: There was even a drawing of the "Maine chain-weathervane"!

Another time, when I was writing of old covered bridges, I told how the horses *clobbered* through the inner bridge, making the floor boards rattle. But the proofreader overlooked my misspelling when I wrote *cloobered* instead of *clobbered*! And since that time I have seen several references to "horses cloobering through the old covered bridges," and I guess the strange word *cloober* might have become part of covered-bridge folklore. And so it goes. There are many things passed off as folklore that were plain mistakes or the invention of some agile mind.

Therefore, in collecting a group of American weather sayings, I have made a special effort to track them down and to separate the true from the false. Our time is already so poor in lore, and there are so many valuable bits of weather information, that to mix the true with jackass jingles and silly superstition would be sad indeed.

The last part of this small book is in the form of an alphabetical folklore dictionary so that you may look up signs involving stars, wind, dew, or whatever else you might wish. Following each saying you will find a **T** (true), **F** (false), or **P** (possible). Each saying is printed in italics while the comments or explanations are printed below in roman type. You might find some disagreement with my comments, but I have simply done my best to research each saying, and the opinions are entirely my own. Many sayings have become popular entirely by word-of-mouth; if you can add any to my list, do send them in to me so that a future edition of this book might be so enriched.

Because I believe the sky was made for beholding and that any weather-wise person enjoys a fuller and more enjoyable life, I recommend to you the poetry and lore of weather.

ERIC SLOANE

Weather Hill Farm
Cornwall Bridge
Connecticut

The Beginning

About half of all the American weather books start out with "that famous Mark Twain saying" that "everyone talks about the weather, but nobody does anything about it." Actually this was not a Twainism at all, but was said by a man named C. D. Warner. Twain quoted Warner in a speech, and the saying became known as one of Mark Twain's from that time on. Twain did, however, say, "If you don't like the weather in New England, just wait a few minutes," and that proverb is most typical of American weather talk. Benjamin Franklin, who said, "Some are weatherwise, some are otherwise," also said, "Know the signs of the sky and you will far the happier be." There seems to be something typically rural American about weather observance: here, instead of *hello,* one most often nods and says, "Nice day today." It has been said that the average American can't start a conversation without referring to the weather first. It is natural, then, that there should also be a good store of American weather folklore.

Being aware that most early-American customs were brought intact from overseas, a student of folklore might wonder how much genuine American folklore there can be. To answer this, I quote from a letter written in 1762 from a father to his son who was preparing a trip to these shores.

"The greatest differences here," he wrote, "you shall find in the weather. You shall need the stoutest of cloathing. The sky and its signs and the seasonal changes are most unlike those to which we are accustomed."

[11]

The constant battle of opposite air

COLD and DRY

the "BATTLE GROUNDS"

GULF STREAM (WARM, WET)

One or two of these cold
Canadian air masses attack
almost
weekly

The American Atlantic coast's *mean* climate is somewhat like
that of England or Europe, yet the local sudden weather changes
and the resulting inability to predict them made farm life most
difficult during the earliest pioneer days. Most of the weather
lore that they had already learned overseas did not seem to apply
to the New World.

Nowhere on earth are there greater variations in temperature
or suddenness of change than in America. New England's climate,
for example, ranges from 110 degrees in summer to minus 55
degrees in winter. Our floods occur in all seasons, our droughts
are severe. Hurricanes born over fifteen hundred miles away in
the tropics seem to reach New England without any loss of

Ireland and England

continuance of the Gulf Stream

England and the European coast are fanned by Gulf Stream influences and air tempered by a long oceanic voyage.

power, sometimes even picking up some punch along the way. Therefore when the pioneer reached our shores, he found climatic conditions so severe that crops or even lives were lost because of the inability to predict weather.

The warm Gulf Stream that tempers the moist climate of the British Isles is strongest off our own Atlantic coast; its effects make our shore line one of mild climate. Yet blobs of cold, dry Canadian air attack this shore-line atmosphere of warmth and wetness on an average of once a week. The clash usually occurs from five to over fifty miles inland, and the results are quick drops in temperature, towering storm clouds, and sudden precipitation.

The variation in our land contours added another note of uncertainty, which further detracted from the pioneer's ability to predict American weather. It might rain hard in some valley of New York State, while the adjacent high ground only a mile away would miss the storm entirely. Or a Massachusetts sea cove might be enveloped in fog and rain while an arm of land a mile away would be in complete sunshine. This sort of thing seldom happens in England.

Over a period of about a century, then, after each area had devised its own lists of weather signs, a native American folklore began to evolve. There is now a definite American weather folk-lore quite separate from that of overseas; what's more, there is still need of it. Our weather bureau can foretell what is over the horizon, and it can spot major storm areas and plot their movements, but when the weather picture is at all uncertain, the experts cannot say for sure what the weather will be in any specific locality.

The national weather map over 50 per cent of the time is an uncertain picture; local radio broadcasts give such phrases as "three out of ten chances" or "scattered showers" in their predictions. Yet what more definite information can be given for a local area than such folklore as:

When Lookout Mountain [Tennessee] has its cap on, it will rain in six hours.

•

When you can see the Connecticut shore [from Long Island] with great clarity, it will rain in about twelve to fifteen hours.

•

Fog from seaward in Maine, don't expect the rain:
Fog from land in warm, batten down for storm.

•

When wild geese fly to the southeast in Kansas, expect a blizzard.

•

Except in winter, a north wind over inland New York and New Jersey brings two full days of drear and drizzle.

•

And so the old-timer can often look overhead, sniff the breeze or look at the sky, and give you a pin-point forecast that no government weatherman would dare risk.

Often you can separate the American folklore from the European by observing a blunt American "Will it or will it not rain?" attitude typical of American practicality. In Britain, where most people go around carrying an umbrella as they might a cane, weather is a thing to live with, and, "Life goes on, rain or not." Of course, life in the United States goes on "rain or not" too, but our meteorological attitude seems to hinge more upon the possibilities of rain than on anything else. We think the British press a bit poetical in its observance of the sky, the clouds, or the sunset each day; on the other hand, our press is always alive with some scheme for man to "conquer the weather."

I once created a series of newspaper articles with drawings about weather, cloud observance, and folklore. I was prompted to do so when a noted publisher remarked that the most important news in any daily paper could well be the weather forecast. Yet the series was turned down by the syndicates, each of whom remarked that the American public does not want to learn about weather or to read folklore; it just wants to know whether it will rain tomorrow.

I found a pleasant reminder of the European attitude toward weather in an "almanack" poem of 1735; the sentiments there have not changed throughout the years.

> Be not anxious, friend,
> About tomorrow's weather;
> Whether our sports it may commend,
> And the fair morn
> Deserve the tribute of the cheerful horn;
> Or drizzly wet compel us to sit
> Around the fire together, both Whigs and Tories,
> And ply the glass,
> Or, time to pass,
> Hum tunes and tell old stories.

The true rural love of weather in America, along with its richness of folklore, seems to have diminished with the passing of individual farming. Farming has become a big business with little place for folklore, but a century ago farming was a way of life, a philosophy of living, rich with lore of the land.

[15]

The Almanacks

Asked to describe the old-time "almanacks" in one word, we might first strike on the word *quaint*. Yet one could call the old almanac about as quaint as we could call a modern dictionary quaint. What with the mentions of moonlore and weather prophecy, you might also think of the word *mystic*. Yet the almanac was as scientific a piece of literature as one could find for its time; it was a calendar based upon moon positions (just as our modern calendar is) with weather indications that had been tallied and averaged over a period of many years (just as our present-day long-range weather forecasts are made). The almanacs were not things collected by a few and ignored by others; they were stock tools of the day, necessary for the carrying-on of any business or even the daily routine of early-American life.

If your clock stopped and your nearest neighbor was ten miles away, you would not carry your clock with its wooden works to his place to set it, for the jiggling would upset its delicate mechanism. Instead you would watch for the sunrise or sunset or moonrise; then, by referring to your current almanac, you would know not only the date, but you could set your clock to the correct second. The tides or the position of the moon means very little to the average person today, yet in the days when there were no electric lights and much of the farming was done in moonlight, you might well have looked forward to the right moonlit night before you planned to harvest this or that field, or to make an overnight ox-cart journey.

Yes, it does seem odd to many now, that the old-timer took his almanac so seriously. Yet he would be astonished at the baseball news and TV commercials and other contemporary trivia that manage to take up so many precious hours of our lives today.

The early, soft-dirt roads of America were completely useless in or after a heavy rainfall. You gave great thought to what day you might choose to go to town, because wheels didn't turn in the old-time-road mud, and you might find yourself stranded for a day or two only a few miles away from home. In fact the roads were so impassable during wet weather that all heavy loads such as lumber or stone were saved till winter and moved by sled over the snow. The almanac was as useful for traveling as the railroad timetable is nowadays.

You might argue that almanacs were for farmers, that the lawyer or shoemaker or storekeeper need not use them. Yet the lawyer, the shoemaker, the storekeeper had to be a farmer also, for he grew his own food and fed his own horses from his own hay-field. Thus everyone in early America was close to the ways of nature, by necessity. People noticed how birds and animals built their homes each year; then they tried to compare these changes with climatic changes in order to benefit from the weather instincts of wild life. For example, in 1733 *Poor Robin's Almanack* said:

> *Observe which way the hedgehog builds her nest,*
> *To front the north or south or east or west;*
> *For if 'tis true what common people say,*
> *The wind will blow the quite contrary way.*
>
> *If by some secret art the hedgehog knows*
> *So long before, the way in which the winds will blow,*
> *She has an art which many a person lacks*
> *That thinks himself fit to make our almanacks.*

We owe many of our weather rhymes to the almanac makers, and although some of these do not actually predict weather, they do add to the richness of weather lore. Here are a few of these meteorological gems:

When it rains while the sun shines, the devil is beating his wife.
He is laughing while his wife is crying.—NEW ENGLAND.

•

The lightning is a yaller gal who lives up in the cloud.
The thunder is a black man that hollers out loud.
The black man kisses the yaller gal and thinks he is a wonder,
He bumps his head against the clouds and that's what makes
the thunder.—VIRGINIA.

•

It's raining, it's pouring, the old man's snoring [thunder].

•

When it snows, the old woman is plucking her white geese.
—MAINE.

•

When the moon wears a halo around her head, she will cry
before morning and the tears [rain] will reach you tomor-
row.—AMERICAN INDIAN.

•

It is raining cats and dogs!—PENNSYLVANIA.

This is believed to be a German mispronunciation of "cats and *ducks*." The Pennsylvanian German people used to say, "It is raining to keep in the cats and bring out the ducks." They also said, "It is snowing for cats and ducks," which meant that the snowfall was sufficient to track a cat or a duck through it.

•

When it thunders, the mountain men are bowling.

This is a New York State saying credited to the story of Rip Van Winkle, although the saying is really older than Irving's story, and he created his "little men who bowled and made thunderous noise" from this old weather saying.

•

There's news in the wind!

From Boston's *Weatherwise Almanack* of the middle 1700's, this saying was prompted from the weathervane, which has letters for north, east, south, and west, all of which happen to spell out N-E-W-S.

Weather Instruments

It has been said that except for electrical communications instruments such as telephones, TV, radio, or radar, many modern weather stations have about the same kinds of instruments as the ones Benjamin Franklin had in his laboratory. He had the anemometer, barometer, hygrometer, and such instruments as are presently used for measuring the qualities and pressures of the atmosphere. Except for the seagoing man, however, who had his barometer, or "weatherglass," few men had instruments at home with which to measure the weather. Yet all around the country there were natural instruments that told of the weather, sending out messages by smell or sound or movement and adding to the weather wisdom of the day. "The sounds and smells and signs of weather," said one almanac, "do set the full rich stage for each day of farming life."

The massive beams of ancient barns shrank or swelled with each rise or fall of the barometer and with changes of atmospheric moisture and sent out messages proclaiming a weather change. The barn builders used wooden pins, or "trunnels" (treenails), to fasten house framework together so that this fastening device could react along with the main members and not split them at the joints. The creak and groan of building timbers throughout a stormy night seldom worried the early American, for he knew that everything was working according to plan in his house framework. But he did know that the nature of the atmosphere was changing. Furniture, too, was designed to "breathe" with the weather; a simple chair might have as many as eight kinds of wood, each planned to react against the other and keep the joints tight. Thus even the cracking of furniture was understood by the weather-wise people of yesterday.

> *Hark how the chairs and tables crack!*
> *Old Betty's nerves are on the rack.*
> *... 'Twill surely rain; I see with sorrow,*
> *Our jaunt must be put off tomorrow.*
> —Dr. Edward Jenner

Any countryman will tell you that you can "hear the weather," that according to atmospheric changes, sound can differ from time to time. On the approach of a storm, the sound-dissipating irregularities of the atmosphere decrease, and sounds come to your ear with a peculiar clarity. As the Tennessee-mountain man says, *"You can hear rain in the air."*

The many sounds of storm are of a subtle and distant lore; perhaps one of the first references is Elijah's "There is a sound of abundance of rain." The American almanacs often mentioned:

> *When the forest murmurs and the mountain roars,*
> *Then close your windows and shut your doors.*

The mention of "forest murmur" and "mountain roar" is typical of the countryman's keen notice of weather phenomena, for a cold-front storm does do just that. Wind starts from higher altitudes and then descends to earth; when a storm approaches, the flat forest simply stirs with a changed air current while the mountain tops (already in the new wind current) have begun to roar.

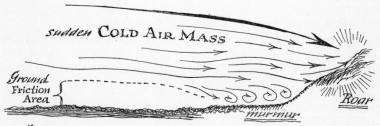

".. when the forest murmurs and the mountain roars."

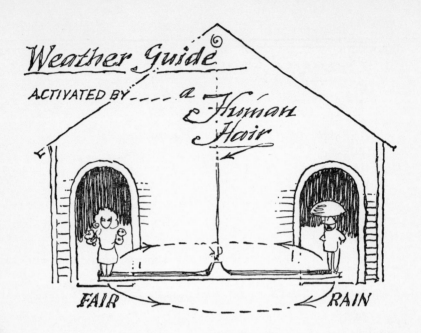

Weather Guide

ACTIVATED BY —— a Human Hair

FAIR   RAIN

Much folklore has evolved with the habit of farming people gathering about the fireplace at night, where the sounds of the outside world come into the room by way of the chimney with extraordinary clarity. The bark of a dog, for example, or the hoot of a distant owl, can often be heard from the hearthside while such sounds may be out of earshot from outside.

Perhaps it is the heat of the chimney that causes a rapid circulation of air, which involves a sharper acoustical property. Some say that it is the loftiness of the chimney top over the various ground-level sounds of wind in the grass and the murmur of lower bushes and trees that bring in distant sounds. Others claim that sound approaching the ear vertically has a different quality from sound approaching the ear horizontally (which seems untrue to this author). Yet one of the most noticeable phenomena of balloon flight is the clarity of sounds from below. Connie Wolf, the lady balloonist from Blue Bell, Pennsylvania, is fascinated by this effect. "The little sounds from below," she says, "such as the conversation between people, the bark of a

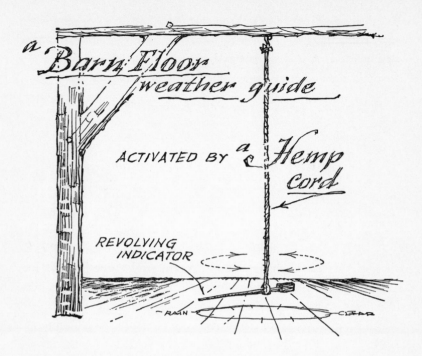

a Barn Floor *weather guide*

ACTIVATED BY a **Hemp** *cord*

REVOLVING INDICATOR

RAIN   CLEAR

dog or the closing of a door, come up to the balloon as if they were only a few yards away!"

The chimney-and-hearth, then, was one of the best-known instruments of weather folklore, either by its sounds, by the way wood burned, by the formation of soot, or by the action of its smoke. People used to say:

A storm makes its first announcement down the chimney.

•

A storm wind settles in the chimney, but a clear wind coaxes out the smoke.

•

One of the farmer's weather instruments was a lump of hemp that was kept in circulating air and made a good hygrometer, or device for recording the water content of the atmosphere. The Indian used a human scalp, and the seaman used a bunch of seaweed; many farmers noted the softness of their tobacco. Fisher-men sometimes used a strand of rope, and farmers often used baling cord. All these materials were affected by moisture and foretold the coming of rain. The Maine farmer said:

When ropes twist, forget your haying. **T**

The sailor's ditty, a version of the same rope weather sign, went:

Curls that kink and cords that bind
Signs of rain and heavy wind. **T**

•

The New England farmer was known to hang a piece of baling cord from the ceiling of his barn, with a heavy stick indicator tied below, just off the barn floor. As the stick turned, the farmer marked on the floor, indications of "rain," "wind," or "dry," etc. This was a version of the European weather guide made in the form of a tiny house with two doors, from which emerged either a boy or a girl, according to the weather promise. This machine used strands of human hair (blond hair reacted best), and the wetness or dryness of the hair caused the figures to swing in and out of the doors.

In England and Europe wind changes are less abrupt and less frequent than they are in the New England section of America. And as our weather may be foretold better by noticing wind direction and change than by any other method of observation, the weathervane became the nerve center for every early-American farmer's weather wisdom. Yet these first weathervanes were not like the ones we are now familiar with—the big metal rooster or whale or trotting horse, which were more for decoration than for accurate weather-lore use, some of them being so heavy that only a strong wind would budge them. The first vanes were made of light pine or cedar and made to swing with the slightest move-ment of air. Because no one knew the directions of east, west, north, and south better than the pioneer farmer did, there were no markers included for this purpose.

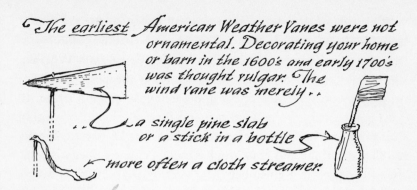

The earliest American Weather Vanes were not ornamental. Decorating your home or barn in the 1600's and early 1700's was thought vulgar. The wind vane was merely . . . . . a single pine slab or a stick in a bottle . . . more often a cloth streamer.

As these old vanes were not ornamental, but were made of fragile wood, there are now none left (as far as this author knows), but only from writings can they be reconstructed in the imagination. There are all too few weathervane sayings remembered from the early days, but some of the nineteenth-century farm diaries refer to wind direction in such rhymes as:

> *A weathercock that swings to the west,*
> *Proclaims the weather to be the best.*
> *A weathercock that swings to the east,*
> *Proclaims no good to man or beast.*

What this tries to say is that any wind from southwest and around the compass to northwest does usually bring dry weather; the easterly quadrant usually brings rain.

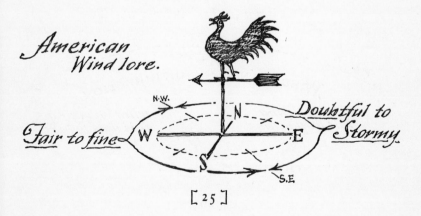

American Wind lore.

Fair to fine

Doubtful to Stormy

This rule of thumb is all too general, however, for the *way a wind is changing* is often as important as the way it is blowing at the moment. That is, whether it is *backing* or *veering*. Whether the wind "backs" or "veers" depends upon the position of the observer with reference to the approaching or passing storm. If you point at where the wind *was* and then at where the wind *is* and your arm has moved *clockwise*, the wind has *veered*. If you do the same thing and your arm has moved counterclockwise, the wind has *backed*. Remember that *"veering is clearing"* and you will be able to predict by this method: a backing wind brings rain. (These sayings refer to storms of a southerly direction.)

> *A veering wind will clear the sky;*
> *A backing wind says storms are nigh.* **T**

Another weathervane saying runs:

> *Winds that swing against the sun,*
> *And winds that bring the rain are one.*
> *Winds that swing round with the sun,*
> *Keep the rain storm on the run.* **T**

This means that a wind that changes in the direction of the sun's movement (from east to west) brings clearing; wind that changes against the sun's movement (blowing from west to east) brings storm and rain. This same rule is referred to in:

> *If the wind back against the sun,*
> *Trust it not for back it will run.* **T**

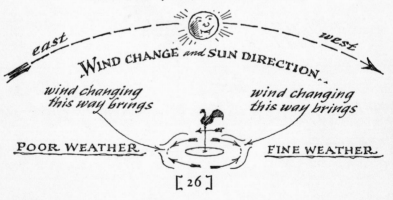

[26]

The early weathervanes were often only a strip of cloth that waved from a pole. They were called wind-flags. In fact the word *vane* comes from the Anglo-Saxon *fane*, which means flag.

It is strange how little the early Americans used barometers for observing the weather, while during the early 1800's these devices had become a popular wall decoration in English homes. Only the Cape Cod weatherglass seems to be America's contribution to barometrical research and design. This object is a glass container that holds water; contact with the outside air is shut off by means of a gooseneck of glass that contains water in contact with the outside air. The battle of pressure differences between the outside air and the inside air causes the water to rise or lower accordingly. *"When the glass spills over, so will the clouds in a little while,"* goes the old Cape Cod saying.

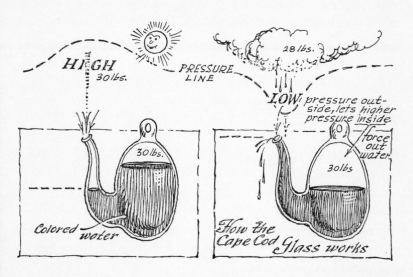

And so the sounds and actions of nature during temperature and humidity changes, along with the few weather devices that could be made around the farm, were about all that the early farmer had to combat the inconsistencies of American weather. A few people thought they could foretell weather by a special power; others could *"feel it in their bones."* As a matter of fact you *can* feel weather in your bones if your bones are extremely sensitive; old wounds and scar tissue react in the same way. Dr. Jenner wrote of such effects of weather changes:

> *"Her corns with shooting pains torment her*
> *And to her bed untimely sent her."*

And Broome said:

> *"A coming storm your shooting corns presage*
> *And aches will throb, your hollow tooth will rage."*

Actually the lowering of pressure during a coming storm is usually not enough to make a noted effect upon a normal, healthy person, but the lowering pressure plus increased humidity is what does the trick. The same stands true for temperature changes, for high heat or coldness is quite bearable to the human body, providing it is *dry*. Damp coldness or damp heat has an instant effect upon us.

In the early days of America, when the countryside was very lush with peat and moss, undrained ditches, and extensive swamps, the country atmosphere was more humid than it is now, and weather changes must have had a greater effect upon the people than they do today. Even in the mid 1700's and for the next century, when people built close to rivers to be near water-powered mills and canals, the effect of water must have made life quite different from that of today. If it were not for our countryside being doomed to disappearance, we might someday evolve a folklore of a drier or waterless living. But along with the vanishing landscape of America, folklore will someday be completely a thing of the past.

A DICTIONARY of American Weather FOLKLORE

(T) ... *true*
(F) ... *false*
(P) ... *possible*

ANTS

When ants travel in a straight line, expect rain; when they scatter, expect fair weather. **F**

There seems to be no reason for this to be true, although many people still use it as a weather sign. In the Ozarks they say, "*Bugs march when the rain is near,*" and in Maine there is a saying, "*Flies scatter in good weather.*" The saying that "*a straight line of ants brings on a rain*" is possibly a combination of those two sayings.

•

APPLES

A tough apple skin means a hard winter. **P**

Nature does seem to be able to predict weather, and the strengthening of skin (bark, etc.) has often preceded a

[29]

hard winter. Since a warm, wet summer does spurt tree growth and expedite sap flow, a resultant thicker skin might well come before a swing of the pendulum of weather averages, and a cold dryness would then be in order.

When apple blossoms bloom at night
For fifteen days no rain in sight.   **F**

•

APRIL

When April blows her horn [thunder]
It's good for hay and corn.   **P**

If it thunders on All Fool's Day [April 1st]
This assures your crop of hay.   **F**

The colder the April, the better the farm crops.   **F**

•

BEES

A bee was never caught in a shower.   **P**

Bees will not swarm before a storm.   **P**

When bees stay close to the hive, rain is close by.   **T**

All these bee sayings are from observation, and the bee-keeper is always a good weather prophet. He will tell you that "*a swarm of bees in July, does little more than bring a dry.*"

•

BIBLE

"*When ye see a cloud rise out of the west, straightway ye say: There cometh a shower: and so it is.*"—Luke, XII: 54.   **T**

In the north temperate zone, where most weather patterns move from west to east, a storm cloud in the west (or a

[30]

western quadrant) will place you directly in the path of the storm.

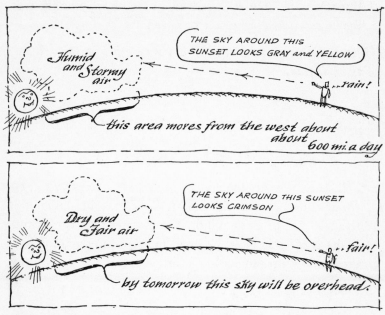

"*When it is evening, ye say, It will be fair weather: for the sky is red. And in the morning, It will be foul weather today: for the sky is red and lowering.*"—Matthew, XVI: 2–3. **T**

Christ, in so speaking, knew that we see the setting sun through air that will reach us tomorrow, as pressure patterns of atmosphere move from west to east. If the setting sun shines through dry air, the sky is reddest; if it shines through moist air, the sky is grayish or yellowish. (These rules apply to the surrounding sky and not the actual disc of the sun.)

BIRDS

South or north, sally forth;
West or east, travel least. **T**

Here is an old saying regarding the migration of geese, which bird watchers say is true. It means that when a flock

[31]

of geese (on migration flight) flies in a true northerly or southerly direction, the morrow will bring clear weather. But when the flock varies its flight to the west or the east, the morrow will bring rain or snow.

Geese (and other migrating birds) fly higher in fair weather than in foul. **T**

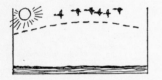 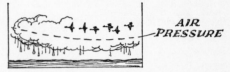

Because pressure lowers as you ascend, the higher you go, the less pressure you will find. Birds seek height in migration to make use of lofty winds, but their ceiling (or altitude limit) is lifted in good-weather, high-pressure air, and lowered in low-pressure, stormy air.

Swallows (and bats) fly close to the ground before a rain. **T**

This is often true, because swallows and bats have very sensitive ear mechanisms, which are affected by sudden changes of air pressure. When there is a sudden drop in atmospheric pressure, they will skim the surface to get as close to the earth as they can and thereby get as high an air pressure as there is at that time.

Sea gull, sea gull, sit on the sand;
It's sign of a rain when you are at hand. **T**

Generally speaking, birds will roost more during low pressure than during high pressure. Before a hurricane great flocks of birds will be seen roosting. Perhaps the lowering pressure or thinning of air density makes flying so much harder; the lessening of natural updrafts would also account for the birds "resting it out."

•

BUDS

Look for a heavy winter when the buds have heavy coats. **P**

This saying from Maine might be truest in that section.

•

CANDLEMAS

This day, celebrated on February 2nd, usually heralds the coldest weather in America. Because of this, it became a great weather-forecasting date, when the farmer looked to the sky and hoped to predict what the worst weather of the year would bring. There is no truth in any of the Candlemas sayings, but Candlemas rhymes have lasted throughout the years, as, for example:

If Candlemas be fair and clear,
Two winters will you have this year. **F**

Because the European winter is often over by this date, while in America the coldest days are yet to come, the early pioneers called the American February a "second winter." The idea of a second winter is also hinted at in this old rhyme:

Half the wood and half the hay
You should have on Candlemas Day. **T**

Very true, for a farmer's winter store should be about half used at this date, and the other half can fortify him for the rest of the bad weather.

•

CATTLE

When cattle lie down as they are put to pasture, rain is on its way. **F**

A cow with its tail to the west, makes weather the best;
A cow with its tail to the east, makes weather the least. **T**

[33]

Wind

This New England saying has much truth in it, for an animal grazes with its tail to the wind. This is a natural instinct, so the animal may face and see an invader; an invader from the opposite side would carry its scent to the cow, in the wind. Inasmuch as an east wind is a rain wind and a west wind is a fair wind, the grazing animal's tail becomes a weather sign.

•

CHRISTMAS

The twelve days after Christmas indicate the kind of weather for the whole year. Each day in that order indicates the trend of weather for each month in regular order for the following year. **F**

The nearer to a new moon on Christmas, the harder will be the rest of the winter. **F**

Green Christmas, white Easter. **F**

A green Christmas makes a fat churchyard. **F**

The assumption here is that people might take off their "longies" when they dress for the Christmas celebration, and catch cold. The greatest number of pneumonia cases were noticed during the two weeks after Christmas whenever the weather was warm at that time.

CLOUDS

The higher the clouds, the better the weather. **T**

Higher clouds indicate both dryness of air and higher atmospheric pressure. Both these qualities are present with fair weather.

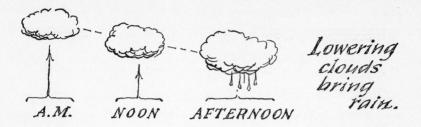

A.M. NOON AFTERNOON

Lowering clouds bring rain.

Clouds moving in opposite directions indicate rain in about twelve hours. **P**

Cumulus clouds smaller at sunset than at noon, a sign of continued fair weather. **T**

No matter what the ground wind, if high clouds are moving from a westerly quadrant, fair weather will persist. **P**

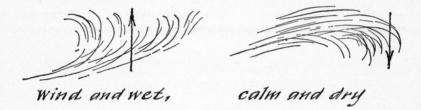

Wind and wet, *calm and dry*

If cirrus mares' tails have ascending streaks or point upward, wind and storm are in the making; if they point downward, calm and dryness are in store. **P**

•

CORN

If corn husks are thicker than usual, a cold winter is ahead. **P**

The Pennsylvanians said, "When the corn wears a heavy coat, so must you." A thicker corn husk is the result of a wetter, warmer summer; a swing of the pendulum to a colder, dryer winter would seem in order in this case.

•

DEW

When the dew is on the grass,
Rain will never come to pass.
When grass is dry at morning light,
Look for rain before the night. **T**

A heavy dew in the evening is the best promise of a dry morrow. Dry grass at night or at sunrise indicates rain before the next noon. This saying is the same as that of England, *"Morn dry, rain nigh; Morn wet, no rain yet."*

•

DOG

Dog days are when dogs go mad. **F**

The Dog Days are that period when Sirius the Dog Star commands the heavens, rising in conjunction with the sun. Starting about July the 26th, this warm summer period lasts about five weeks. As drought time was often plague time too, many people got the superstitious idea that sickness came with the Dog Star, along with madness.

When a dog eats grass, it is a sign of rain. **P**

You might be surprised that the author finds this saying "possible." His reason is that *an old dog* with rheumatism will find that pre-storm lowering pressure and increased humidity increases his physical discomfort to the amount of an over-all feeling of sickness and pain. The only thing an animal can do in sickness is to purge his system by inducing vomiting; hence the eating of grass.

•

EASTER

Before Easter, winter is not to be trusted. **F**

•

Thunder in February frightens the maple syrup back into the ground. **P**

This is a New England jingle with truth to it. Not that the sap is really frightened, but sap flow in the maple tree is a very sensitive phenomenon, and unseasonably warm weather (enough to cause heat updraft and thunderclouds) might well cause sap flow to slacken. Maple-sap flow depends upon freezing during the night and thawing during the day.

•

FISH

Near the surface, quick to bite,
Catch your fish when rain's in sight. **P**

Fish in both fresh and salt water tend to sport and bite more eagerly before a rain than directly after one.

When the wind is in the north,
The skillful fisher goes not forth;
When the wind is in the south,
It blows the fly in the fish's mouth. **P**

These lines should have meaning, for they were written by that eminent fisherman, Izaak Walton.

•

FLIES

Flies bite more before a rain. **T**

This rule does not always apply, but insects do cling more during moist weather, as flying is more difficult. Heat causes human sweating, which makes you a more appetizing target. These two reasons, plus a release of more body odors when the atmospheric pressure on your body lowers, will all add up to the rule that flies and insects are more bothersome just before a rain than at any other time.

•

Fog

Fog from seaward, weather fair;
Fog from land brings rainy air. **P**

Much fog in the autumn,
Much snow in the winter. **P**

These two are from Massachusetts; they are usually true in that state, but there seems to be no reason to classify them as general weather truth.

Fog in the morning, sailor take warning;
Fog in the night, sailor's delight. **P**

There are too many reasons for fog for this saying to be classed completely true. For example, it is generally accepted that "*a summer fog for fair and a winter fog for rain.*"

Three foggy mornings will bring a rain three times harder than usual. **P**

This one from a New Jersey almanac; three foggy mornings in a row, it reasons, would need that much stronger a rain to purge such static atmosphere.

•

Friday

If the sun sets clear on Friday, it will storm on Sunday. **F**

The first Friday of each month is an almanac index for the trend of weather the rest of the month. **F**

These two sayings from New York State are silly sayings, but they are still fun to observe.

•

FROGS

When you hear the first frogs in the spring, the frost is out of the ground. **P**

Generally this is true, yet it also depends upon location and altitude.

•

GRASS

Cobwebs on the grass are a sign of frost. **T**

Not always, of course, but the "cobwebby grass season" is during late Indian summer, which usually occurs after the first frost and before the second frost.

•

GROUND-HOG DAY

Originally called Candlemas Day (February 2nd).

On this day, in Europe, the bear and badger were supposed to come out to see their shadow. If the animal sees his shadow, this is supposed to frighten him back for another six weeks, and cold weather will last that long. In America the saying refers just to the ground-hog (woodchuck). **F**

•

GROUSE

When the grouse drums at night, a big snow will fall in the early morning. **F**

This is an American Indian saying.

•

HAIR

When human hair becomes limp, rain is near. **T**

There is an American Indian saying that "when locks turn damp in the scalp house, it will rain on the morrow." Hair (particularly blond hair) is still used in hygrometers for measuring humidity.

•

A HALO BRINGS PRECIPITATION

HALO

Sun or moon halos indicate a coming rain (or snow): the larger the halo, the nearer the precipitation. **T**

This is more likely to be true during warm weather than during midwinter. You are seeing the sun (or moon) through the high ice crystals of cirriform clouds. When these cover the whole sky, it is the sign of an approaching warm front when a long, slow rain will occur. The American Indian puts it thus:

When the sun retires to his house [halo], it is because it is going to rain outside. **T**

The advent of a moon halo after a pale sunset is a fairly certain rain sign. Dr. Edward Jenner said:

"Last night the sun went pale to bed
The moon in halos hid her head." **T**

•

HURRICANE

June, too soon;
July, stand by;
August, look out!
September you will remember.
October, all over. **T**

This names the hurricane months in America.

Face a hurricane wind and point to your right; you will point to the storm center as it moves along. **T**

This is true of all low-pressure storms, but it is most useful in watching the progress and plotting the exact direction of a hurricane's eye.

•

INDIAN SUMMER

If we don't get a good Indian summer in October or November, we will get it during winter. **F**

Truly American folklore, *Indian summer* is a vague term because no one is completely certain as to its exact date, its origin, or even what the term implies. Generally speaking, it is an unseasonable spell of hot, dry weather that occurs in October. Europe has its counterpart in *"Saint Luke's little summer,"* which begins on the eighteenth of October and ends on the twenty-eighth. The day (October 28th) is supposed to be a day of rain. In America Indian summer was first noted as "a period of late summer heat that occurs right after the first frost." As for the name, some say it originated from its peculiar haze, which resembled "the smoke of Indian fires in the hills." Another explanation is that this was the period when the Indians started out on their fall hunting trips.

•

INSECTS

When the katydid says "Kate," he announces ten days till a frost. **P**

Kate-ee-did-n't . . 87°
Kate-ee-did . . . . 72°
Kate-ee . . . . 65°
Kate . . . . 58°
Ka . . . . 55°
mute below 55°F.

} Summer night temperature (°F)

[41]

Coldness numbs all insects and first slackens their calls. When "kate-ee-did!" is reduced to a single "Kate!" it is because of the lowering temperature. The first frost might well be near.

Crickets are accurate thermometers; they chirp faster when warm and slower when cold. **T**

They are extremely accurate. Count their chirps for fourteen seconds, then add forty, and you have the temperature of wherever the cricket is.

When ladybugs swarm
Expect a warm. **F**

•

July

If it rains on July 26th, it will rain for the following two weeks. If it is dry, expect two weeks of dryness. **F**

•

June

Wet June, dry September. **F**

•

Killing

Kill a beetle and it will rain. **F**

Step on an ant and it will rain. **F**

Kill a snake and turn its belly to the sky for rain. **F**

Kill a snake and its body will move till sundown. **F**

•

Leaves

When the leaves show their backs, it will rain. **T**

When trees grow, their leaves fall into a pattern according to the prevailing wind. Therefore, when a storm wind

[42]

Prevailing wind ———⟶ 🖋 *leaf.*
  ~*smooths out the* *leaf.*
Rain wind ⟵ *leaf* ⟵
  shows the leaves' underside. 🖋

(which is naturally a non-prevailing one) occurs, the leaves will be ruffled backwards and show their light undersides.

•

LIGHTNING

Lightning is attracted to mirrors. **F**

Lightning in the south, brings little else but drought. **T**

Not drought really, but at least it brings no rain. Because most temperate-zone thunderstorms follow a west-to-east movement, lightning from anywhere except a western quadrant will pass you by without bringing rain.

Yaller gal, yaller gal, flashin' through the night,
Summer storms will pass you by unless the lightnin's white. **P**

This refers to "heat lightning," which is simply lightning from a storm that is passing you by, or has passed you by, seen far to the south, north, or east. Seen through dusty storm air, it appears red. White lightning is usually that which is seen through clearer air and from a storm which is in a western quadrant and on its way toward you.

Red lightning foretells a dry spell. **P**

Not a dry spell really, but the storm not reaching you. Explanation of this phenomenon is the same as in the previous saying: you are simply seeing lightning from a storm that is passing by.

Thunder curdles cream. **F**

Lightning sours milk. **F**

These two sayings are still believed by most people. Although the old-timers used to cover milk or cream "from

[43]

lightning," there seems to be no scientific proof that lightning or thunder has any effect on either milk or cream. In the days of no refrigeration, however, the atmospheric effects that caused the storm itself (low pressure, humidity, and heat) would also hasten the spoiling of milk products and make them vulnerable to curdling. So perhaps it was the weather rather than the thunder or lightning!

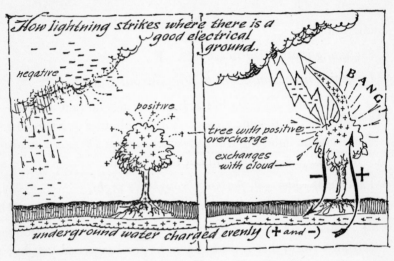

Where lightning strikes, go dig your well. **P**

It has been often true that wherever lightning hit, spring water was close underneath. Lightning is the release of an uneven electrical charge into a more stable reservoir of current. As a vast underground spring cannot change its charge as rapidly as the ground above, a tree whose roots contact a spring makes an excellent target for an exchange of currents and an equalization of potentials.

•

MARCH

In like a lamb, out like a lion;
In like a lion, out like a lamb. **F**

•

MAY

Dry May, wet June.   **F**

Cold, wet May,
Barn full of hay.   **T**

May 11, 12, and 13 are days of cold weather.   **F**

A saying that began in England, where these days were called The Feast of the Three Icemen. The saying persisted here in America after 1816 ("the year without a summer") when a heavy snowstorm during those three days blanketed New England.

•

MILKWEED

Milkweed closes at night before a rainy spell.   **P**

The same, however, can be said of the dandelion, clover, and other plants that change their leaf attitude on the approach of rain. The English version is:

Pimpernel, pimpernel, tell me true
Whether the weather be fine or no.   **T**

Indeed, the pimpernel closes its petals when the humidity exceeds 80 per cent. Laurel and rhododendron close according to the degrees of coldness.

•

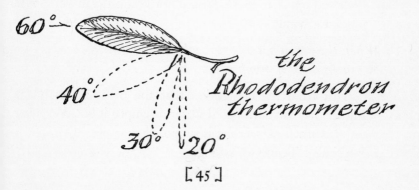

the Rhododendron thermometer

Moon

If the moon rises pale, expect rain;
If it rises clear, expect fair. **P**

Pale moon doth rain,
Red moon doth blow;
White moon doth neither rain nor snow. **P**

"Pale moon" implies that it is seen through a veil of thin cirriform clouds such as go before a warm air front, which ends in a long, slow rain.

Clear moon, frost soon. **P**

Moonlit nights have the heaviest frosts. **T**

Farmers watch for frost during the full moon. Frosts occur when the night is calm and the air clear.

Sharp horns do threaten high winds. **T**

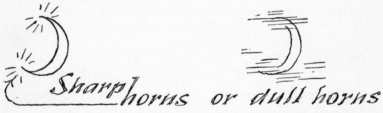

Sharp horns or dull horns

When the crescent moon's ends, or "horns," are clear and sharply defined, it means that high-altitude air is unusually clear as the result of high-speed winds aloft. As winds begin aloft and lower to earth, "sharp horns" on the moon would predict a windy day.

When the moon lies on her back,
She sucks the wet into her lap. **F**

This from the contention that the moon looks like a dipper that can either hold water or empty it out. With her points turned down, one is supposed to expect rain. There is a similar Tennessee saying:

The crescent moon spills or holds the rain for the coming month. **F**

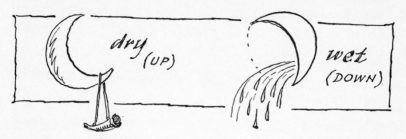

When you can hang your powder horn on the moon, do just that. **F**

This is a famous Indian saying. What it means is that when the moon's horns are upright enough to "hang something on one," hang up your powder horn, and don't try stalking game, because the woods will be dry for want of rain. Indians did most of their hunting when the ground was wet.

Sir John Herschel devised a table for predicting weather by observing the moon. **P**

This table, credited to Herschel (although he did not claim responsibility), was used in America with great faith. The Pennsylvanian Germans made ornamental "fractur writing" copies of it. For what it is worth, here it is:

First consult your almanac, and observe the following:

If the new moon, first quarter, full moon, or last quarter in summer occurs between

12 and 2 A.M.	...... *fair*
2 and 4 A.M.	...... *cold and showers*
4 and 6 A.M.	...... *rain*
6 and 8 A.M.	...... *wind and rain*
8 and 10 A.M.	...... *changeable*
10 and noon	...... *frequent showers*
12 and 2 P.M.	...... *much rain*

2 and 4 P.M.	......	*changeable*
4 and 6 P.M.	......	*fair*
6 and 8 P.M.	......	*fair (if wind northwest)*
8 and 10 P.M.	......	*rain (if wind south or southwest)*
10 to 12 midnight	......	*fair*

If the new moon, first quarter, full moon, or last quarter in winter occurs between

12 and 2 A.M.	......	*frost unless wind is southwest*
2 and 4 A.M.	......	*snow and wind*
4 and 6 A.M.	......	*rain*
6 and 8 A.M.	......	*stormy*
8 and 10 A.M.	......	*cold if wind westerly*
10 and noon	......	*cold and high winds*
12 and 2 P.M.	......	*snow and rain*
2 and 4 P.M.	......	*fair and mild*
4 and 6 P.M.	......	*fair*
6 and 8 P.M.	......	*fair and frosty if wind is north*
8 and 10 P.M.	......	*rain and snow if wind is south*
10 to 12 midnight	......	*fair and frosty*

The moon loses its outline ten hours before rain. **P**

Not infallible, but often true. The coming of a warm-front ceiling first renders the moon like a ground disc (rain about thirteen hours away); then it loses its shape completely (rain about ten hours away).

•

Moss

Moss dry, sunny sky;
Moss wet, rain you'll get. **T**

This is a southern-mountain saying. Moss (like human hair) is an excellent material for absorbing atmospheric moisture. In Maine the same saying goes for seaweed.

•

[48]

NIGHT

When the night has a fever, it cries in the morning.   **T**

Although this is an old Indian saying, it probably refers to the meteorological truth that if the temperature increases between 9 P.M. and midnight, rain follows.

•

NORTHERN LIGHTS

Northern lights bring cold weather with them.   **P**

This one, the scientists will argue with this author about; for although he can find nothing to back him up on it, he has found cold waves and an aurora over the northern horizon very often occurring at the same time. His contention is that an extremely strong cold wave will carry Arctic particles of auroral quality with it. Although the particles are much higher than the mass of cold air, there is still a long-range magnetic field present. During the past five consecutive auroras (seen as far south as Connecticut) there was a very strong flow of Arctic air present.

•

OCTOBER

Full moon in October without a frost,
No frost till full moon in November.   **F**

October has twenty-one fair days.   **P**

Indian summer probably prompted this one.

•

ONIONS

Onion skins very thin,
Mild winter coming in;
Onion skins very tough,
Winter's going to be very rough.   **P**

This Midwest saying has become almost as popular as the one about the woolly bear. Another Pennsylvania-Dutch

[49]

version is from Baer's *Agricultural Almanack*; it goes this way:

On New Year's Day scoop out half an onion, one for each month, and place salt therein. After twelve days, the onions in which the salt has dissolved will be the wet months to come. **F**

•

Spill salt into each scooped half:

Jan.　Feb.　Mar.　Apr.　May　June

July　Aug.　Sept.　Oct.　Nov.　Dec.

Salt is supposed to dissolve first in the wet months of the coming year.

PONDS

Ponds often turn over during a storm. **P**

Inasmuch as the bottoms of ponds often rise to the top during a heavy downpour, country people call this phenomenon a "turning over." A cold rain falling into a warm pond will settle to the bottom while the warm lower layer will rise to the top. During late summer this "turning over" illusion is most pronounced.

Some storms cause tides in fresh-water lakes. **T**

The effect is like a tide, but the actual cause is the wind. If a lake running east and west is battered by a strong west wind, the body of water piles up at the east end in the form of a high tide.

•

R

The chill is on from near and far
In all the months that have an R. **T**

[50]

This was an early-American saying that ended up in restaurant-menu lore regarding the eating of oysters. "One should eat oysters," the saying went, "only during months that contain the letter *R*." Or, as the restaurants put it on their signs, "Oysters *R* in season." The explanation is that all other months have sufficiently warm weather to make oysters liable to have large amounts of dangerous sewage germs in them. Cold water descends and lifts debris to the top.

•

RAIN

Morning rain is like the old lady's dance;
It doesn't last very long. **P**

This one is from Maine. They also say of this same weather phenomenon:

If the rain waits till noon to visit, prepare for a long visit. **P**

This means that when you have a threatening morning but the rain doesn't appear till after noon, it will continue into the night and morrow.

Rain long foretold, long last;
Short notice, soon past. **T**

This one is generally true, because the warm-front rain flows overhead for about ten hours before its tail brushes the ground with rain, and then the warm-air-mass rain lasts for a day or so. The cold-front rain, however, is unannounced, and although it falls harder as a rule, it is soon over.

•

RAINBOW

Rainbow in the morning,
Shepherd take warning;
Rainbow toward night,
Shepherd's delight. **T**

[51]

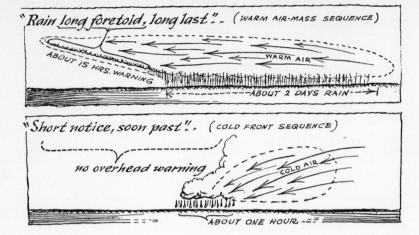

"*Rain long foretold, long last*". (WARM AIR-MASS SEQUENCE)

ABOUT 15 HRS. WARNING

WARM AIR

ABOUT 2 DAYS RAIN

"*Short notice, soon past*". (COLD FRONT SEQUENCE)

no overhead warning

COLD AIR

ABOUT ONE HOUR

The modern version of this verse substitutes *sailor* for *shepherd*. Because storm centers usually move from the west, a morning rainbow would have to be seen from a storm already in the west with the eastern sun shining on it. That storm would reach you. But an evening rainbow is seen in the west amid a storm that has already passed you. Therefore, a "shepherd's delight."

It is bad luck to point at a rainbow. **F**

This is a New York State saying, taken from the Indians. If you point at a rainbow, so the story goes, and the storm god disapproves of you, the rainbow will disappear, but so will you!

•

ROOSTER

When the rooster crows at night,
He tells you that a rain's in sight. **F**

If the cock crows going to bed,
He wakens with a watery head. **F**

Cockcrow before two in the morning
Of two days wet it is a warning. **F**

Some say that a sudden drop of atmospheric pressure or an increase in humidity will waken a rooster into crowing.

•

Saint Swithin's Day

If it rains on St. Swithin's Day (July 15th), it will rain for forty days. **F**

From *Poor Robin's Almanack* in 1697, this had been an English saying observed in America too. St. Swithin (the Bishop of Winchester) had a great reverence for rain and asked that he be buried outside the church wall "so that the rain might falleth" upon his grave. This was done, but in the year 971 on July 15th, his body was removed to a tomb within the church, whereupon a great storm broke and lasted for forty days.

•

Sap

When the wind is in the east,
Then the sap will run the least;
When the wind is from the west,
Then the sap will run the best. **T**

From Vermont, this is part of maple-syrup lore. Sap flows when the nights are freezing but the days are thawing. Such a phenomenon occurs almost always during a west wind in New England.

•

Sheep

When the sheep collect and huddle,
Tomorrow will become a puddle. **P**

This is a western saying, an adaptation of the Indians':

When the buffalo band together, the storm god is herding them. **P**

•

SIGHT

The farther the sight, the nearer the rain.   **T**

Particularly near the sea, when distant spots loom and appear closer, it is not a sign of clear weather, as many think, but a sign of rain. Haze over the marine horizon during a hot day shows a good degree of evaporation and weather stability. The mixing of air by instability and the lack of evaporation produces clearer air, greater vision, and promise of rain on the morrow.

•

SKY

Evening red and morning gray
Sets the traveler on his way;
Evening gray and morning red
Brings down rain upon his head.   **T**

Enough blue sky for a Dutchman's breeches gives the storm just half an hour.   **T**

If you can see blue sky during rainfall, you are seeing it through scud clouds in the rear of a low-pressure area.

Mackerel skies and mare's-tails
Make ships carry low sails.   **F**

Mare's-tail cirrus can be a fair-weather sign if they are few and scattered. Only a skyful of either cirrus or mackerel (cirro-cumulus that resembles rippled sand) can mean that a storm is approaching.

•

SMELL

When ditches and cellars smell most, a long rain is near.   **T**

As the weight of high-pressure (fair-weather) atmosphere keeps a certain amount of the odors trapped, a lessening of

pressure (as before a storm) will release odors from walls, swamps, ditches, cellars, etc. One almanac put it:

When the ditch offends the nose,
Look for rain and stormy blows.

•

SMOKE

When smoke descends, good weather ends.   **T**

The instability of pre-storm pressures and humidity keeps smoke from chimneys or bonfires from rising quickly, finally to curl downward in the face of a storm wind.

•

SNAKE

Bury a snake, good weather to make,
Hanging it high brings storm clouds nigh.   **F**

Because snakes often writhe for a long time after death, the legend is that "a snake will move till sundown." Many other superstitions also involve dead snakes. Country people often bury a dead snake "to keep rain away," but it is possible that the original reason was really just to keep away the smell.

•

SNOW

If the first snowflakes of a snowstorm are large, this means the storm will last; smallish first flakes indicate a short storm. **P**

Although this is not always true, large flakes are merely masses of smaller flakes stuck together, and the turbulence and wetness that caused the flakes to stick both result in a storm condition of lasting variety.

The day of the month on which the first snowfall occurs indicates the number of days of snow for the whole coming winter. If the first snow falls on the thirteenth, for example, there will be thirteen snowstorms during the coming winter. **F**

On a stove melt a pint of snow from the first snowfall; the number of bubbles rising to the surface will tell you the number of snowfalls for the season. **F**

If snow commences near noon, it shall be heavy.

Or as the almanac said:

If snow begins in mid of day,
Expect a foot of it to lay. **P**

You can't generalize on this one, but because heavy precipitation is often the result of a strong cold wave and this wave moves in upon the warmer air of midday, the resulting storm is liable to be a strong one.

•

SOAP

When drops collect on soap,
For rainfall you can hope. **P**

Not so much with modern soap, but when people made their own soap, humidity in the atmosphere collected rapidly on the surface of a cake of soap, particularly after a long dry spell.

•

Soot

When soot falls down the chimney, rain is near. **P**

The theory is that delicate soot is held in place by air's heavy pressure and dryness, along with some atmospheric magnetism. Therefore when air pressure lowers and dampness enters the picture, electric atmospheric phenomena lessens too, and the soot is loosened.

•

Sound

Sound traveling far and wide
A stormy day this does betide. **T**

This verse from old English farm books is a saying with merit, for you actually can "hear bad weather approaching," according to country people. Faraway sounds such as train whistles, droning airplanes, or distant birdcalls sound hollow or as if heard down a long corridor, and predict a long siege of rain, such as a warm-front storm.

•

Spiders

When spiders forsake their webs one day, look for rain the next. **F**

Spiders spin webs on the grass during Indian summer. **T**

As told in Eric Sloane's *Look at the Sky*, the tiny gossamer spider is known for its webs that appear on the grass as dewy strands during Indian-summer mornings. In fact the word *gossamer* comes from "goose summer," or the early-English name for our Indian summer period.

•

Squirrels

When squirrels lay in a big store of nuts, look for a hard winter. **F**

Squirrels just do the best they can, and some years have better nut seasons than others. Yet the old-timers still observe the activities of the squirrels as a sign of winter weather.

•

STARS

The Dog Star brings drought.   **P**

Not that the star itself causes drought, but when the Dog Star, Sirius, is most evident, droughts are most liable to occur, because of the lack of rainfall at that season.

When the stars begin to hide
Soon the rain it will betide.   **T**

Increasing humidity and haze precede a spell of rain and cause the stars to fade.

•

SUN

The sun "drawing water" indicates the coming of rain.   **F**

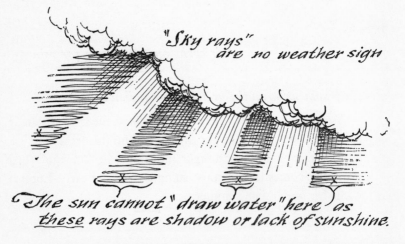

"Sky rays" are no weather sign

The sun cannot "draw water" here as these rays are shadow or lack of sunshine.

The sunlight always draws water by means of evaporation. Usually where we see shafts of light and shadow, the sun is *not* drawing water. Because there must be less evaporation in the presence of shadow, when you see such shafts of dark with sunlight between, you might say, "See—there the sun is *not* drawing water."

When the sun sets unhappy [with a veiled face], the morning will be angry with storm.—Zuni Indians   **T**

Because weather usually moves from west to east, you see the setting sun through atmosphere that will reach you later on; when that "atmosphere to come" is moist and veiled by high cirrus clouds, you will find rain commanding the morning.

A sunshiny shower
Won't last out the hour.   **T**

If the rain clouds are so scattered and confined as to admit sunshine between them, the cloud cover is indeed breaking up, and the storm is about to cease.

•

SUNDAY

If it storms the first Sunday of the month, it will storm every Sunday of the month.   **F**

This is an old circus saying, also applying to "the first Saturday of the month." Silly as it seems, records have been kept showing it to be as much as 90 per cent true over a period of ten years, according to circus people.

•

SWINE

Hogs should be slaughtered after the second frost, in the dark of the moon.   **P**

Country slaughtering is always done after the warm spell that follows the first frost, assuring coolness to keep the hanging meat from spoiling. The "dark of the moon," however, probably referred to the superstition that moon rays spoil meat, which is untrue. The first Department of

Agriculture *Weather Book* said that "moonbeams produce certain chemical results that spoil fish and some kinds of meat." This superstition was printed by that organization as late as 1903.

•

TELEPHONE WIRES

Telephone wires [or telegraph wires] hum and whine when a weather change is due. **T**

When cold, dry air arrives, wires tighten and cause a high-pitched humming sound. With the arrival of cold air a short storm usually occurs at the onset of the air mass. This singing of wires is loudest in winter.

•

THUNDER

Thunder at morn,
Wind is born;
Thunder at noon,
Rain comes soon;
Thunder at eve,
A tempest will weave. **F**

Thunder in spring,
Cold will bring. **F**

Thunder is of almost no value in the prediction of storm paths, except that thunder from a western quadrant is from a storm that is most certain to reach you.

•

TREES

Trees grow dark before a storm. **T**

Generally speaking, the landscape reflects the sky, either by water or by the glossiness of a solid tree pattern. This truth, however, is a very subtle phenomenon.

•

TURKEY

If turkey feathers are unusually thick by Thanksgiving, look for a hard winter. **F**

*A dark breastbone in a Thanksgiving Day turkey indicates a
hardy winter to come.* **F**

•

WATER

*When the spring that's low
Begins to flow,
Then sure we know
It will rain or snow.* **P**

This is a southern-mountain saying. Generally speaking,
this is not true, but there are many springs and wells that *do*
respond to pre-storm pressures and begin to flow just before
precipitation. This is supposedly caused by the drop in outside atmospheric pressure.

•

WEDDING

*A rainy wedding day
Makes the skies of marriage gray.* **F**

An old hillbilly saying; indeed, weddings have been
called off in Arkansas because of the weather.

•

WILD AZALEA

*When the wild azalea shuts its doors,
That's when winter tempest roars.* **P**

•

WIND

*When the wind is in the east
'Tis neither good for man nor beast.* **P**

This is most true along the Atlantic coast where an east wind blows wetness into the land areas, while it presages a warm air-mass storm from the south (which usually brings a long-lasting type of rainfall).

An easterly wind is like a boring guest that hasn't sense enough to leave. **P**

In many coastal areas, the storm with easterly winds proves the most long-lasting. It frequently shifts between northeast and east for two days.

High-altitude winds soon descend to earth. **T**

Winds do tend to originate aloft and settle to earth. By observing the direction of high-altitude clouds, you may tell what the wind direction at earth level will be in a few hours or the following day. This effect explains the following New Hampshire saying:

The storm alights on the mountain, and walks into the valley before the rain arrives. **T**

The east wind brings aches and pains. **P**

Humidity plus lowering pressure does seem to affect the nerves, causing old wounds, etc., to begin hurting. The almanac said that

With coming storm your aching corns presage,
And aches will throb, your hollow tooth will rage.

A west wind is a favorable wind. **T**

This is the temperate-zone prevailing wind of favorable weather. It is the wind that follows all storms and is associated with clearing and good spirits. Benjamin Franklin said, "Do business with men when the wind is in the west, when the barometer is high."

A west wind like an honest man, goes to bed at sundown. **P**

This favorable wind is lessened by the cooling off of land areas after the sun lowers and sets.

The worst winds are at the end of the storm. **P**

In an ordinary gale the wind often blows hardest when the barometer is just beginning to recover from a low.

North to west, sugar's best;
South to east, flow is least. **T**

Maple-sap flow depends on a sharp freeze at night and a good thaw during day. This happens with a north or west wind and cannot occur with a south or east wind.

Wind direction is the major sign for storm prophesy. The first United States (Department of Agriculture) Weather Book lists the following rules for using wind to predict weather.

1. Westerly winds (southwest to northwest) are fair-weather winds.
2. When during a storm the wind shifts from east to west, clearing follows.
3. Over a great part of the United States a steady and strong south-to-east wind will bring rain within thirty-six hours.
4. Easterly winds bring rain; northeast winds in winter bring heavy snow.

•

Woolly Bear

The amount of brown on the woolly bear (that part in the middle) foretells the severity of the coming winter. **P**

At least many weather experts have been mystified by this one. The wider the middle band, the milder the winter.

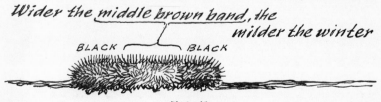

Wider the middle brown band, the milder the winter

BLACK   BLACK